Pepper
learns good habits

Don't suck your thumb, Kate. It's a very bad habit!

Children, go and wash your hands. Lunch is served.

Pepper! What are you doing?
Get off the table.

Bob, don't talk with your mouth full.

Yiew!

Don't pick your nose, Dan! Mama says it's a bad habit.

Pepper, don't
suck your
thumb. It's a
bad habit too!

Now, now.
Why don't you
take turns?
Pepper, you can
be the signalman
when Bob runs
the train.

Let's help Pepper
put away his toys.

Thanks!